Just
North
Enough

Harold + Melanie

ADOPT A PET

Art.. ? Craft... ?
whatever it takes.

Tough it out!
— Sue

Elina '03

The bears in this book, if at one time real, are now entirely fictitious. Any resemblance to real bears, living or dead, is entirely coincidental.

Published by
Potato River Press
P.O. Box 728
Stillwater, MN 55082

First Edition: October, 2000

This book is printed on acid-free paper.

ISBN   0-9704800-0-8

Printed in the United States of America

Dedicated to
Todd, Tara, Tyler,
and to Marian,
the memories of Dick and Walker,
and coffee-breaks at the Farm.

" You have way too much fun. "
— Barb

Introduction

or Why I Draw Bears

It is a usual, quiet afternoon in October, 1997, upstairs in Stillwater, Minnesota's American Gothic Antiques. I don't want to make little leather bridles for model horses anymore, so I walk to Marshall's area in the rear of the store. Marshall sells old hunting magazines. One from the 1920's has a handsome woodcut illustration of a calm grizzly bear. I have a BFA degree. Maybe I can draw a bear...

Fate places a blank piece of card stock and a sharpened pencil in the desk drawer...

The first drawing is very bad. I am stubborn. The third drawing is almost O.K. Time to go home. I put the magazine back in the rack, pack up, and leave. But the next shift I bring my own drawing paper and pencils. Draw, draw. Roger appears - telling stories to his four pals. He's a wood-worker. Third shift... Has wife and cubbies. All I do is watch and listen. Then it's time to draw and write.

It was Roger who sneaked me into a parallel forest where I'm allowed to scribble at will. But the other bears growl, "My turn! My turn!" Here come Al and Beth and Mike and Sheila. And Carla and Carl, Steve and Old Tom. They, too, want their portraits drawn and stories told.

I do what they say - almost every day.

They're bears....

Shirley Chats With Tourists:

Shirley felt that she could speak for the group.

"It isn't that we don't like raspberry jam — we love it.

"And... not that you have any... but, what we'd like just now is some nice rotten meat - wild or domestic."

Love of old Jazz
led him into wilder places
than the Northwoods — and
he got shot at just as often.

Once again James
walked out of her
life. She knew he
wouldn't miss her. Not
at all. But it was dark. And
the Big Cliff was right over there.

He admired the
great bear rug
but couldn't make
a bid on
Uncle Billy...

Was serious gardening
really worth the cost?

Was the bank still open?

All Barb ever wanted
was a little more control.

Roger shied away
from things on a stick.
The State fair was Hell.

"Escape! Escape!," was all
he could think.

He'd purchased
the hat at
an auction.

off of a farm wagon.

Mysteries abound.

Tom was not
pro-violence, but he
liked it on T.V.

Too long
in retail.
Time to move on.

©2000
Sue Rowe

At last they had
the Power.

Now they needed
the Plan.

Bets were being taken.

She forced herself
to take only one
beagle appetizer.

Damn Mickey +
his magic wand.

The Perils of Earl

Seed potatoes...

Earl could feel October
in these early April spuds.

Sigh.
And bring on Summer!

Earl's ducks were
finally all in
a row.

It was not how
he'd planned to
spend the day.

Earl's visit to the circus
ended early — when the
crowd clapped way too long
+ loud for three sad
dancing ducks.

   He'd known their Mother.
Joy was not an option...
The circus chopped
into his soul.

Autumn was warm, red, yellow, and cruel. The spuds were gorgeous and plentiful. Everywhere.

Prices plummeted.

The Canadian Honkers "bonked" good-bye to Earl. They'd spent the night at his pond and in his cornfield.

He'd told them of the huge loss he'd take again this year.

He was beyond fall sad.

And yet Earl
Continued to farm.

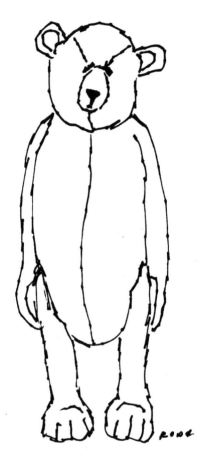

Well, God, yes, he
knew he wasn't "real."
But Andy knew he actually
existed - and so life
could go on. Such as
it was.

Willie <u>was</u> the Blues...

Chad never said "No"
to a doughnut.

Sadly, "wear stupid cap" _was_ part of the contract.

His presentation was
not funny, but
the beavers
laughed and laughed.

Not merely a
Garden Club Matron.

He politely refused
Marcia's offer of a
muskrat sandwich.

Muskrat gave him gas.

Early on Reed decided
to be a jazz musician.
Mother was not pleased,
but Grandmother flew
him to Chicago.
One way... Sigh.

ROWE

Harold was not amused.

A new mini-van was in his parking spot. People were fishing in his favorite chunk of the river.

At least their children looked delicious. Life's trade-offs in the Northland...

He galloped toward the tykes.

Ted sighed ... There was
no easy answer to the
Beaver Question ...

Bubbles ponders the void.

"Some day I might
bake cookies,
but don't buy
milk yet,"
    I said.

Ralph At The Bakery:

Sweet rolls or doughnuts...?
Sweet rolls or doughnuts...?

what the hell is a bagel?

Life was once again
knocking him to the ground.

Frank had heard
all the River talk
he could stand.

He wrestled the
pike from the
old logger, gave all
a semi - obscene
gesture, + headed
out of Stillwater.

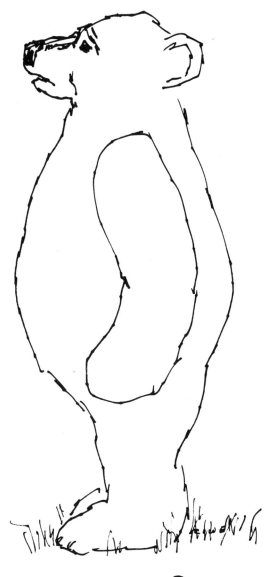

Papa Frank, Papa
Frank, where
are you going?

Even this far North
he could hear jazz
in Big Muddy.
What he couldn't
learn from lumber
he would learn
from Lionel.

Frank realized
that if not a
great drummer,
he was finally
really good.
He'd head North
in the Spring.
To drum with
the really big sticks.

And inspire
Cubbies all around.

Yes, the truth hurt
some times, but Mary
was a   strong   bear
and c   the
pain   that
Rod   that
spec   er.
Sh
w
E
o
t
g   r.

ROWE

No longer finds
humor in fluids.

I'm simply too busy
to be overwhelmed..

She always wears a
lovely bow because it
makes her look
so dainty.

May 6, 1954

Tony requests a
new campsite.

To heck with hiring
another motivational speaker.

Bob decided to recruit
the aid of a motivational
candy bar — with nuts.

All Steve wanted
now was his own
pot of coffee, a
quiet comfy booth,
and to be left alone
till early March.

Why Larry talked to the lake.

Why did
he have to
have a
mission?
Wasn't mere
survival
enough?

The lake
listened quietly,
and thanked
him for the
visit.

God, he loved
the lake.

SUE ROWE

Bach freed
Billy's soul —
Now he was
truly wild.

That was <u>not</u>
what one does
with a turtle.

Just because
Mom baked it
doesn't mean it's good.

Grandpa
would go
out at night,
but, where,
he'd never say.

An Irony in the North land

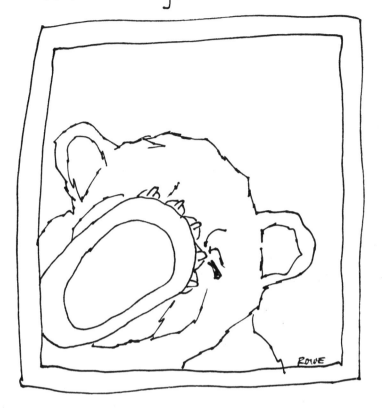

When little Emily tossed her "bear" slipper at Old Nell the real fun began.

Nell's response was normal, and now she's gone far far away...

The big toy bear sat in the dark + pondered his uncertain future.

SUE
ROWE

The group balked
when Henry suggested
they spend the tourist's
money on a chainsaw.

A bite of
   young frog

Turned the
   evening

Even darker.

After some long
hours of argument
Shelby allowed
Tim to handle
the hound.

There were just
so many good
Bitches at the
Garden.

She, of course,
could hold her own.

The cute one we
called "Muffin,"
before he ate
our dog.

April 26, 1954

of course
Fritz knew that
eaves-dropping
was impolite.
But the hunters'
chat appeared
to concern him
personally...

ROWE

First Date at the Bait

Dearest — over here —
Chunks of chunks of
super-chewy gobs of
chopped piles of our
favorite congealed flavors
of red-orange-green
Gummi Bears oh bears
yes. yes.
Every where.
Just for us. And
Especially for you
oh large and lustrous
Love.

Could we hope
for more tomorrow?
And tomorrow?

The small fawn
showed no fear
Logging truck
I shouted

Sue Rowe

— Ben

Too Many Bears —
Not Enough Guns

He couldn't bring himself
to say the side-kick slot
was filled...

Deep thoughts
at
the
dump.

Late in the evening
Earl could be persuaded
to tell tales of his
participation in
The Great Beaver
uprising.

Of course he'd cry.
That came to be expected.

Damn all beavers.
Damn all beavers...

Soon, yes,
they'd learn
to fear the
patient fool.

Pia <u>was</u> the answer!

I've got enough power.
Bring on the fun!

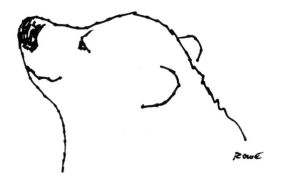

The cubbie sniffed
the Kitchen.

Grandma's cookies
didn't stand a chance.

Shortly
Alma realized that...
that... merely simply
sulking
would require even
too much effort.

She sat... and glazed over.

Suddenly the air
was filled with the
rythmic chanting of
Danish pastries.

Oddly, even canoeists
were beginning to piss
him off...

They called
him The Dark
Bear of Mystery
Bend, and that
was O.K. with
Arlene.

Harold looked at
the motorcycle for
over an hour.

Something had to give.

He strode down the
courthouse steps
cursing ducks and all
their lawyers.

So now it was
dark and he
was alone —
except for
the two dozen
ducks...

Once upon a time
in Teddy Land Mort
stole a little knife.

It caused quite
the stir →
but it got her elected.

Randy winked at the
vixen & by God if she
d.dn't wink back!

Tales from The Old Bear

She was so old
her stuff was
back In Style.

Running her paw over the bowl's rim Anna could find no flaws. It was a magnificent piece + she must have it.

She'd deal with Bert later.

Even with his dark past
Bob considered himself a useful
bear. Just not around kittens.
Growl...

Old Freddie
The Twisted Teddy.

Of course he could
still juggle bunnies.

She planned to grow
old with grace & dignity.

Come hell or high water.

They couldn't say
she hadn't tried.

Sis felt badly for the
others, 'cause they
didn't make the cut...

Send some furry fun to a friend:

JUST NORTH ENOUGH order form

Mail to: Sue Rowe Studios, Box 728, Stillwater, MN 55082

Please send me ____ copy(ies) of JUST NORTH ENOUGH @ $23.00 each (U.S. funds). Prices include shipping and handling. Minnesota residents please add 6 1/2% sales tax.

Enclosed is my check/money order payable to Sue Rowe Studios, in the amount of $_____.

Name_____

Address_____

City_____State_____Zip_____

JUST NORTH ENOUGH order form

Mail to: Sue Rowe Studios, Box 728, Stillwater, MN 55082

Please send me ____ copy(ies) of JUST NORTH ENOUGH @ $23.00 each (U.S. funds). Prices include shipping and handling. Minnesota residents please add 6 1/2% sales tax.

Enclosed is my check/money order payable to Sue Rowe Studios, in the amount of $_____.

Name_____

Address_____

City_____State_____Zip_____